STEP ON A CRACK

by

Suzan Zeder

Dramatic Publishing Company
Woodstock, Illinois ● Australia ● New Zealand ● South Africa

IMPORTANT BILLING AND CREDIT REQUIREMENTS

All producers of the play *must* give credit to the author of the play in all programs distributed in connection with performances of the play and in all instances in which the title of the play appears for purposes of advertising, publicizing or otherwise exploiting the play and/or a production. The name of the author *must* also appear on a separate line, on which no other name appears, immediately following the title, and *must* appear in size of type not less than fifty percent (50%) the size of the title type. Biographical information on the author, if included in the playbook, may be used in all programs. *In all programs this notice must appear:*

"Produced by special arrangement with
THE DRAMATIC PUBLISHING COMPANY, INC., of Woodstock, Illinois."

To My Mother

FOREWARD

I offer this play to you with a profound respect for the complexity of childhood. As a writer, I have tried to confront the child within myself as honestly as possible in order to bring you a child of this moment. A funny, crazy, wildly imaginative child who arms herself with a full-blown fantasy life to fight her way through real life problems. Ellie's difficulty adjusting to her new stepmother is as classic as Cinderella and as timely as tomorrow.

I have been deeply gratified by audience reaction to this play. I remember one day after a matinee performance a child and a young woman sat quietly together in the empty lobby of the theatre. After a few moments the child turned to the woman and said, "That could have been about us." "Yes," the woman replied, "Do you want to talk about it?" The child thought for a moment and finally said, "Okay. Let's go home!"

Perhaps I might offer a bit of advice to potential producers and directors of this play. If a child actress with sufficient maturity, skill, and depth can be found; by all means cast her. But do not let this be a limitation. I have seen this play work equally well with a young adult in this role. Perhaps you might consider a college student with a bit of training behind her. I have even seen an impressive performance by a high school student.

If an adult actress is used I would urge her to spend some time with children; to notice how they move; to listen to the patterns of their laughter; to watch them closely in the whirlwind of temper tamtrums, in joyous flights of fantasy, and in quiet moments of frustration and despair. All of these things are part of Ellie. It is my sincere wish that Ellie be played as a real child and not as an adult comment on childhood.

Above all, please have fun with this script . . . I have!

— *Suzan Zeder*

Musical Version of STEP ON A CRACK

This edition of Suzan Zeder's widely acclaimed play has been slightly revised by the playwright. it is dedicated to those producers who wish to stage this play.

A musical version of STEP ON A CRACK was introduced by Seattle's PONCHO Theatre at the 1978 New Orleans Convention of the Children's Theatre Association of America. It is now available with the purchase of this playbook and the score by John Engerman, with songs by Suzan Zeder.

Cues for music and songs are indicated in this text by asteriks*. The Engerman/Zeder score contains all dialogue bridges or alterations required within the text of the play. Producers whishing to stage this musical version may obtain rights and scores from Anchorage Press Plays, Inc.

There is an additional royalty charge for each performance of the musical version.

CHARACTERS

Ellie Murphy: A ten year old girl.
Max Murphy: Her father, about thirty-seven.
Lucille Murphy: Her stepmother, about thirty-five.
Lana: Ellie's imaginary friend.
Frizbee: Another imaginary friend.
Voice: Ellie's alter-ego.

SETTING

Ellie's house
A bowling alley
The streets

TIME

The Present

The premiere production of STEP ON A CRACK was presented on March 14, 1974, at Southern Methodist University, Dallas, Texas, with the following cast:

Ellie .... Martha LaFollette
Lucille .... Mary Jo Lutticken
Max .... Ron DeLucia
Lana .... Jackie Ezzell
Frizbee .... John Rainone
Voice .... Jennifer Glenn
The production was directed by Susan Pearson.
Set Design by .... John Tillotson
Costume Design by .... Nina Vail
Faculty Advisor .... Charley Helfert

The cover graphic is the set as designed for STEP ON A CRACK
   by John Tillotson

STEP ON A CRACK

By Suzan Zeder

The main playing space consists of two areas: ELLIE'S bedroom and a living room. A free standing door separates the two areas. The set should be little more than a brightly colored framework. Each space has a ladder which is hung with the various costumes and props used throughout the play.

ELLIE'S room is the larger of the two spaces. It is outlandishly decorated with old pieces of junk, flags, banners, old clothes etc. which have been rescued by ELLIE from her father's junk yard. The room is a mess, strewn with piles of clothes and junk. Up center is a larger box marked TOYZ'. At the far side of the room there is a stool surrounded by a simple frame. This frame indicates a mirror. This is VOICE'S area. VOICE never moves from this spot until the very end of the play. It would be helpful to have a microphone and P.A. speaker here. VOICE will make all of the sound effects used during the play.

The living room, MAX and LUCILLE'S space, is conspicuously neat. A coffee table and a few chairs indicate this area.

❋
At Rise: ELLIE, MAX, LUCILLE and VOICE are onstage. MAX holds one end of a jumprope, the other end is tied to the set. VOICE sits on the stool. LUCILLE sits in the living room area. ELLIE jumps as MAX turns the rope for her. She jumps for a few seconds to establish a rhythmn.

MAX: Cinderella . . . Dressed in yeller . . . Went downtown to meet her feller. Cinderella . . . Dressed in yeller . . . Went downtown to meet her feller. [*MAX continues to chant and ELLIE to jump as LUCILLE speaks.*]

LUCILLE: Grace, Grace . . . Dressed in lace . . . Went upstairs to wash her face. Grace, Grace . . Dressed in lace . . . Went upstairs to wash her face.

VOICE: [*Joins in*] Step on a Crack . . . Break your Mother's back. Step on a crack . . . Break your Mother's back. Step on a Crack . . . Break your Mother's back! [*ELLIE jumps out of the rope and hops jour times firmly.*]

ELLIE: CRACK! CRACK! CRACK! CRACK! Step on a crack, break your STEPmother's back!

VOICE: Red Light! [*All freeze.*]

VOICE: Ellie Murphy used to be a perfectly good little girl. Green Light! [*All come to life for a second MAX and ELLIE take a few steps toward each other.*]

VOICE: Red Light! [*All freeze.*]

VOICE: Her mom died when Ellie was just four years old, and everybody
          felt so sorry for her. They said "Oh you poor little girl." And they
          brought her extra helpings of cake and lots of presents. Ellie lived with
          her Pop, Max Murphy, boss of Murphy's Wrecking and Salvage Company.
          Green Light! [*During the next few lines MAX and ELLIE play a game of*

ELLIE: Not it!

MAX: Knock, knock . . .

ELLIE: Who's there?

MAX: Banana.

ELLIE: Banana who?

MAX: Knock, knock . . .

ELLIE: Who's there?

MAX: Banana.

ELLIE: Banana who?

MAX: Knock, knock . . .

ELLIE: Who's there?

MAX: Orange.

ELLIE: Orange who?

MAX: Orange you glad I didn't say banana?

VOICE: Red Light! [*All freeze.*]

VOICE: They played tag and went bowling; they ate T.V. dinners and
          practiced baseball for six years and they were very happy. Green Light!
          [*ELLIE and MAX mime practicing baseball*]

MAX: Listen Midget, if I told you once I told you a million times, you
          gotta keep your eye on the ball. [*He throws an imaginary baseball, ELLIE
          hits it and MAX follows the ball with his eyes and sees LUCILLE.*]

MAX: Fantastic!

VOICE: Red Light! [*All freeze.*]

9

VOICE: About two months ago Ellie went to camp and Pop met a pretty lady who taught music. Green Light! [*ELLIE and MAX hug goodbye. ELLIE moves up her ladder and scratches her bottom, she mimes writing.*]

ELLIE: Dear Pop, Today we went camping in the woods and guess where I got poison ivy? [*Max moves over to LUCILLE*]

MAX: [*Shyly*] Hi, my name is Max, Max Murphy.

LUCILLE: Pleased to meet you Max, I'm Lucille.

VOICE: Red Light! [*All freeze.*]

VOICE: And Pop liked Lucille and Lucille liked Pop. Green Light! [*ELLIE puts a blindfold over her eyes*]

ELLIE: Dear Pop, I can't go swimming today cause I got pink eye.

VOICE: Ellie came back from camp and everything in her whole life was different. [*ELLIE, MAX and LUCILLE play blind man's bluff.*]

ELLIE: 5, 4, 3, 2, 1 . . . Ready or not here I come.

MAX: We're over here.

ELLIE: Where? Am I getting warmer?

MAX: Naw, you're a mile off.

ELLIE: Am I getting warmer?

VOICE: Red Light! [*All freeze.*]

VOICE: Pop and Lucille got married. Green Light! [*MAX and LUCILLE move into wedding positions. They mime an exchange of rings and kiss.*]

ELLIE: I said am I getting warmer? Hey Pop where did you . . . [*ELLIE takes off the blindfold and sees them kissing. She claps her hand over her eyes and giggles.*]
VOICE: Red Light! [*All freeze.*]

VOICE: Everything was different. Lucille cooked well balanced meals with vegetables. She kept the house neat and sewed buttons on all Ellie's clothing. Pop liked Lucille a lot, he wanted Ellie to like her too but somewhere deep inside Ellie's head this little voice kept saying . . . Look how pretty she is . . .

ELLIE: Look how pretty she is.

VOICE: Look how neat she is . . .

ELLIE: Look how neat she is.

VOICE: Pop likes her much better than he likes you.

ELLIE: No!

VOICE: Oh yes he does! [*ELLIE turns away*]

VOICE: Ellie Murphy used to be a perfectly good little girl. Green Light! [*MAX exits. ELLIE moves into her room and picks up a Whammo paddle-ball. LUCILLE moves into the living room area and sets up a music stand and practices singing scales. She has a beautiful voice.*]

ELLIE: [*Hitting the paddle-ball*] 235, 236, 237, 238, 239, 240, 241, 242, 243, 244, 245, 246 . . . [*ELLIE misses, sighs, and starts again.*]

ELLIE: 1,2,3,4,5,6,7,8,9,10,11,12,13,14 . . . [*ELLIE misses, sighs, and starts again.*]

ELLIE: 1, 2, 3, 4, 5, 6, 7, 8, 9, 10, 11 . . . [*ELLIE misses.*]

ELLIE: I'll never make 300! 1, 2, 3, 4, 5, 6 . . . [*ELLIE misses. She crosses to the mirror. VOICE mimes her gestures.*]

ELLIE: If I could make 300 I'd be famous. I'd be the world's champion. I'd be rich and famous and everyone in the whole world would come up to me and . . . How de do? Yes, it was very difficult, but I just kept practicing and practicing. No, it wasn't easy. [*LUCILLE sings louder.*]

VOICE: Considering all the racket SHE was making.

ELLIE: Considering all the racket SHE was making.

VOICE: How could anyone expect to concentrate with all that toot toot de doot?

ELLIE: How could anyone expect to concentrate with all that toot toot de doot..

VOICE: What does she think this is Grand Opree or something? [*ELLIE clutches her throat and mimics LUCILLE, she warbles off-key.*]

ELLIE: Laaaaa . . . Laaaaaaa, Laaaaaaa, Laaaaaaa. [*LUCILLE hears her and stops.*]

LUCILLE: Ellinor? Did you call me?

ELLIE: No. [*LUCILLE resumes the scales. ELLIE gets an idea. She crosses to the toy box and pulls out a wierd assortment of junk; a couple of old hats, a black cloak, a deflated inner tube, silver shoes, and a set of Dracula fangs. ELLIE dresses herself and makes a couple of menacing passes at the mirror. VOICE mimics her action. ELLIE sneaks out of the room and up behind LUCILLE.*]

ELLIE: I am Count Dracula and I have come to suck your blood!

LUCILLE: [*Startled*] Oh my!

ELLIE: Did I scare you?

LUCILLE: You startled me.

ELLIE: What are you doing anyway?

LUCILLE: I am just running through a few scales.

ELLIE: Do you have to?

LUCILLE: Well, yes. The voice is just like any other instrument, you have to practice every day.

ELLIE: You call that MUSIC? All that toot toot de doot?

LUCILLE: Well, scales aren't exactly music but . . .

ELLIE: [*Singing very off-key.*] "Everybody was Kung Fu Fighting." Uh . . . uh . . . uh . . . uh . . . hu!**

LUCILLE: Well, ummm that's very nice but . . .

ELLIE: [*Lying on her back with feet in the air.*] "I've got tears in my ears from lying on my back crying out my eyes over you."**

LUCILLE: Ellinor, what in the world are you wearing?

ELLIE: Pretty neat huh? I got this stuff from Pop, it's from the yard. He said I could keep it. You should go down there, he's got some great stuff.

**These songs should be constantly changed to songs that are currently popular.

12

LUCILLE: Oh Ellinor, you have such a nice room and so many lovely toys. Why do you keep bringing home all this junk?

ELLIE: This isn't junk! It's perfectly good stuff!

LUCILLE: But people have thrown it away.

ELLIE: That doesn't mean it isn't any good! How would you like to be thrown away?

LUCILLE: When I was your age I had a collection of dolls from all over the world. I used to make clothes for them and make up stories about them. You know I still have those dolls. I gave them to my brother for his children, maybe I could write to him and we could . . .

ELLIE: Dolls! Ugghhh! I like this stuff better. Besides most of it isn't mine. Most of this belongs to Lana and Frizbee.

LUCILLE: Oh?

ELLIE: This tire is for Frizbee's motorcycle and these hats and beautiful shoes are for Lana. She's a movie star and she needs these things in her work.

LUCILLE: I thought you told me she was a Roller Derby Queen.

ELLIE: She's both! Oh, the Dracula fangs . . . they're mine.

LUCILLE: Just put them away when you are through. Have you finished cleaning up your room yet?

ELLIE: Ohhh I have been busy.

LUCILLE: You promised to do it before your father came home.

ELLIE: Pop doesn't care. He never used to make me clean up my room.

LUCILLE: Look, why don't I give you a hand. Together we can do it it no time.

ELLIE: No way! You'll just make me throw stuff out. [*ELLIE walks back to her room and stands in her doorway.*]

ELLIE: Nobody gets in my room without a pass! [*She slams the door, LUCILLE sighs and turns back to her music.*]

VOICE: Red Light! [*All freeze.*]

VOICE: She doesn't like you. [*ELLIE is drawn to the mirror.*]

ELLIE and VOICE: Pick up your room you messy little girl. Why don't you play with dolls like normal children? You're freaky and you like junk. You could have such a lovely room if it wasn't such a mess.

VOICE: She could never like a messy little girl like you. Green Light! [*LUCILLE resumes her scales. ELLIE listens for a second and begins to mimic her.*ELLIE leaps to the top of the toy box and warbles in a high squeaky voice. FRIZBEE pops up from under a pile of dirty clothes.*]

FRIZBEE: Bravo! Bravo! What a beautiful voice you have! You sing like an angel! You sing like a bird, only better. I kiss your hand. May I have your autograph?

ELLIE: Why certainly young man! [*ELLIE scribbles on his back*]

ELLIE: "To Frizbee from Ellie, the world's greatest opera singer."

FRIZBEE: I will treasure this forever. Here this is for you! [*FRIZBEE pulls a flower from nowhere and presents it to ELLIE.*] *

LANA: [*Her voice comes from the toy box.*] Everybody out of my way. [*ELLIE jumps off the box, the lid flies open and LANA pops out.*]

LANA: Ellie Murphy, the great opera singer, do you have anything to say to our viewers at home? *

ELLIE: How de do.

LANA: How did you get to be such a great opera singer?

ELLIE: Oh it was very difficult. The voice is just like any other instrument you have to practice every day. [*FRIZBEE presents her with a bowling pin.*]

FRIZBEE: Ellie Murphy I am pleased and proud to present you with this singer of the year award.

ELLIE: Dear friends, I thank you and I have only one thing to say, I deserved it. I practiced every day . . . [*LUCILLE starts to sing a beautiful melody . ELLIE moves toward the mirror.*]

ELLIE: I practiced until my throat was sore from singing and . . .

VOICE: Red Light! [*All freeze.*]

VOICE: You'll never be as good as Lucille. [*VOICE snatches the pin away from her.*]

14

VOICE: She's a much better singer than you are. Green Light.

ELLIE: [*Grabs for the pin*] This is MY prize and I deserve it! [*They struggle with the pin*]

ELLIE:[*To LANA and FRIZBEE.*] Hey you guys! [*They rush to her aid. The pin is tossed in the air and FRIZBEE catches it.*]

rRIZBEE: Ellie Murphy I am pleased and proud to present you with this singer of the year award.

ELLIE: Thank you for my prize. It is neat! [*There is the sound of thunderous applause. LUCILLE crosses to ELLIE's door and knocks. The applause stops instantly.*]

LUCILLE: Ellinor? [*LANA and FRIZBEE freeze.*]

ELLIE: Who goes there?

LUCILLE: May I come in?

ELLIE: What's the password?

LUCILLE: Please?

ELLIE: [*Peeking out*] Have you got a pass?

[*LUCILLE enters and looks around.*]

LUCILLE: Who were you talking to?

ELLIE: Lana and Frizbee.

LUCILLE: [*Playing along*] OH! Are they still here?

[*Frizbee pops his head up and makes a rude sound, then disappears into the box.*]

ELLIE: Sure, Frizbee just did a raspberry.

LUCILLE: Oh? [*LANA crosses in front of LUCILLE making ugly faces at her.*]

ELLIE: And Lana's making faces . . . like this and this and this . . . .
[*LANA goes into the toy box. LUCILLE crosses to the middle of the room crouches down and speaks into empty air.*]

LUCILLE: Were you two helping Ellie clean up her room?

15

ELLIE: Lucille, they're not here. They went into the toy box.

LUCILLE: [*Playing along a bit too much*] Oh I see. Do they live in the toy box?

ELLIE: [*Nonplussed.*] It's too small to live in there. They just sit there sometimes.

LUCILLE: Oh. Please Ellie, let me help you. We'll have this place cleaned up in no time. Now where does this go?

ELLIE: No deal! You throw out too much!

[*ELLIE starts putting things away.*]

LUCILLE: Oh Ellinor, you've lost another button. I just sewed that one on too.

ELLIE: It is a scientific fact that some people are allergic to buttons.

[*ELLIE looks hard at LUCILLE*]

Hey, Lucille, how old are you?

LUCILLE: [*A bit taken aback.*] Uhhh, well, I'm thirty-five.

ELLIE: [*Very serious*]   Boy that's old.

LUCILLE: Well, it's not that old.

ELLIE: Do you use a lot of make-up?

LUCILLE: I use some.

ELLIE: A lot? Do you put that goopy stuff on your eyes to make them look big?

LUCILLE: Would you like me to show you about make-up?

ELLIE: Uhhhgg. NO! Make-up is for girlies and OLD people.

LUCILLE: Come on Ellinor, let's get this room done before your father gets home. [*MAX enters with a football helmet and a feather duster for ELLIE.*]

MAX: Anybody home?

ELLIE: Too late! [*ELLIE runs to greet him and jumps into his arms. He gives her the helmet and duster, as LUCILLE enters ELLIE hides them behind her back and sneaks them into her room.*]

MAX: Hey Midget.

ELLIE: Neato. Thanks.

[*LUCILLE approaches to hug him.*]

LUCILLE: Hello dear, you're early.

MAX: Be careful, I'm a mess. I gotta wash up. [*LUCILLE gets him a rag. He wipes his hands and then kisses her. He sits down to take off his boots. ELLIE enters with his house shoes.*]

MAX: Hey Ellie, what's the matter with your shirt?

[*MAX points to an imaginary spot on her shirt, ELLIE looks down and MAX tweaks her nose.*]

MAX: Ha! Hah! Gotcha! Can't have your nose back. Not till you answer three knock knocks . . . Let's see . . . Knock, knock . . .

ELLIE: [*With her nose still held.*] Who's there?

MAX: Dwain.

ELLIE: Dwain who?

MAX: Dwain the bathtub I'm dwouning.

ELLIE: Hey, I got one. Knock, knock.

MAX: Who's there?

ELLIE: DeGaulle.

MAX: Degaulle who?

ELLIE: [*Crossing her eyes*] De-gaulle-f ball hit me in the head and dats why I talk dis way.

MAX: Ohhhh.

ELLIE: Oh I got another one Pop. Knock, knock. . .

LUCILLE: [*Jumping in.*] Who's there? [*ELLIE shoots her a nasty look and turns away.*]

ELLIE: Nobody.

LUCILLE: [*Puzzled*] Nobody who?

ELLIE: [*Insolently*] Just nobody that's all! [*MAX and LUCILLE exchange a look.*]

MAX: I've still got your nose.

ELLIE: [*Back in the game*] Give it back you Bozo.

MAX: Nope you gotta get it. [*MAX pretends to hold her nose just out of reach. ELLIE jumps for it. MAX tosses it to LUCILLE.*]

MAX: Here Lucille, catch! [*LUCILLE, confused, misses it.*]

LUCILLE: Huh? Oh I'm sorry.

The game is over and Ellie scowls.]

ELLIE: Pop, do I have to clean up my room? Can I get you a beer? Can I watch T.V.? Do I have to throw out all my good stuff?

MAX: Whoa! What's going on?

ELLIE: Can I watch T.V.?

MAX: Sure.
LUCILLE: Max, I have been trying to get her to clean up her room for days.

MAX: Awww it's Friday afternoon.

LUCILLE: Max.

MAX: Clean up your room Ellie.

ELLIE: Awww Pop, you never used to make me.

MAX: Sorry Midget. This ship's got a new captain.

ELLIE: Awww Pop!

MAX: Do what your mother says.

ELLIE([*Under her breath*] She is not my real mother.

MAX: What did you say?

ELLIE: Nothing.

MAX: Hey, maybe later we'll do something fun.

ELLIE: Can we go bowling?

MAX: Maybe.

ELLIE: Oh please, oh please, oh please! We used to go all the time. Pop and me, we were practically professional bowlers. We were practicing to go on Family Bowl-O-Rama, on T.V.

MAX: Clean up your room and we'll talk about bowling later. [*ELLIE trudges into her room. MAX sits down and LUCILLE massages his back.*]

LUCILLE: You're early.

MAX: Yep, and I have a surprise for you.

LUCILLE: For me, Max? What is it?
MAX: You gotta guess. It's something we've been talking about.
        [*ELLIE interrupts. She is wearing a long black cape, a tall hat and a scarf. She holds a piece of metal pipe.*]

ELLIE: Ta Dah! Presenting the Great Mysterioso! You will see that I have nothing up my sleeve. See this pipe? See this scarf? Here hold this hat lady. [*ELLIE hands the hat to LUCILLE*]

ELLIE: Now I take this scarf, just an ordinary everyday magic scarf, and I put it over this piece of pipe. Now you both will blow on it. [*MAX and LUCILLE blow on the scarf.*]

ELLIE: I say some magic words. OOOOOBLEEEDOOOO OBBBBBLEEE-DAY ZOOOOOBLEEDA! Zap! Zap! Zap! [*ELLIE flips the pipe over her shoulder, it lands with a loud crash. She grabs the hat and places the scarf in it.*]
ELLIE: Presto! No more pipe! Ta Dah! [*ELLIE displays the empty scarf. MAX and LUCILLE clap.*]

MAX: I thought you went to . . .

ELLIE: I found this stuff while I was cleaning. Pretty neat huh?

19

LUCILLE: That was very nice Ellie.

MAX: Ellie, Lucille and I are talking.

ELLIE: What about?

MAX: ELLIE!

ELLIE: I'm going. I'm going! [*ELLIE goes back to her room. MAX takes some folders out of his pocket.*]

MAX: Do you remember that travel agent I said I was going to talk to?

LUCILLE: Oh Max, do you mean you did it?

MAX: Did I talk to him? Ta Dah! Little lady, you and I are going on a honeymoon. We are going to Hawaii.

LUCILLE: Hawaii? Oh Max!

MAX: Just look at this, "American Express twenty-one day excursions to Honolulu and the islands." That's our honeymoon, that is if you want to go.

LUCILLE: Want to? I have always wanted to go to those places. But can we? I mean should we? Right now?

MAX: Why not? I've been saving for a trip and I think I can take about three weeks off. Now's as good a time as ever.

LUCILLE: I'm not so sure we ought to leave Ellie right now.

MAX: She'll be fine. I can get someone to stay with her and after all she's in school. There is this lady, Mrs. Dougan, she used to stay with Ellie when I'd go on hunting trips. I'll call her tomorrow.

LUCILLE: I just don't want her to think that we are running off and leaving her.

MAX: Don't worry, I'll talk to her.

LUCILLE: Right away . . . that is if you are serious.

MAX: You bet I'm serious. I got all this stuff didn't I? Look at some of these tour deals. You get everything: air fare, meals, hotel, an air conditioned bus . . .

LUCILLE: Oh look at that sun, and all that sand. What a beautiful beach.
[*ELLIE enters clutching a T.V. Guide.*]

ELLIE: Guess what! Midnight Spook-a-thon has a double feature tonight!
The Curse of Frankenstein and the *Return of the Mummy's Hand!* Isn't
that neat? Can I watch it Pop?

MAX: [*Hiding the folders*] Uhhh Sure, why not.

LUCILLE: What time does it come on?

ELLIE: [*Nonchalantly*] Oh early.

LUCILLE: What time?

ELLIE: [*Quickly*] Eleven-thirty.

LUCILLE: That's awfully late.

ELLIE: Tomorrow's Saturday. And besides Pop said I could.

LUCILLE: We'll see.

ELLIE: You always say that when you mean no. What are you guys doing?

MAX: We're talking.

ELLIE: [*Seeing the folders*] What this? [*LUCILLE starts to show them to
her and MAX snatches them away.*]

MAX: Papers, papers of mine. Ellie is your room cleaned up yet?

ELLIE: No! Gee whiz! I'm going. I'm going! [*ELLIE crosses back to her
room.*]

LUCILLE: Max, why didn't you talk to her?

MAX: Oh I don't know, I just hate it when she yells.

LUCILLE: Yells? I thought you said it was going to be alright.

MAX: It is! I just have to kind of talk to her about it . . . when she's in a
good mood.

LUCILLE: If you really think it is going to upset her, let's not do it now.
We can always go later.

MAX: I said I was going to talk to her and I will . . . [*MAX crosses to ELLIE'S room LUCILLE follows slightly behind.*]

MAX: Ellie . . . uhhh

ELLIE: I'm not finished yet but I'm cleaning!

MAX: Looks like you are doing a good job there. Want any help?

ELLIE: Huh? [*ELLIE finds the duster and dusts everything and then starts dusting MAX.*]

MAX: Ellie, umm Lucille and I . . . uhhh we were thinking that it might be a good idea if . . . if . . . we went . . . bowling! Tonight!

ELLIE: Hey, neato!

MAX: After you clean up your room.

ELLIE: I'll hurry. I'll hurry. [*MAX leaves the room with LUCILLE shaking her head.*]

LUCILLE: Why didn't you tell her?

MAX: Let's wait until we know exactly when we're going.

LUCILLE: I don't want her to think that we are sneaking around behind her back.

MAX: I'll tell her. I just want to pick my own time. [*ELLIE starts out the door.*]

VOICE: Red Light! [*ELLIE freezes.*]

VOICE: Something fishy's going on. They don't want you around. They're trying to get rid of you . . . Green Light.
[*ELLIE stares into the mirror*]

MAX: So that's your surprise. How do you like it?

LUCILLE: Oh Max! [*LUCILLE hugs him. ELLIE enters.*]

ELLIE: Ahem!

MAX: What do you want?

ELLIE: I just came to get a shovel.

LUCILLE: What do you need a shovel for?

ELLIE: I'm cleaning! I'm cleaning! [*MAX turns her around and marches her back into the room.*]

LUCILLE: Please Max! [*They all enter the room.*]

MAX: Ellie, I want to talk to you . . . . .[*ELLIE shines his shoes.*]

MAX: ELLIE!   [*ELLIE looks up at him and gives him a goofy look.*]

MAX: I just want to tell you . . . . I tell you what! If you clean up your room right now then we'll all go get ice cream or something!

LUCILLE: [*Exasperated.*]   I have to stop at the market anyway. I'll go make a list. [*LUCILLE exits.*]

MAX: And now once and for all . . . listen here tough guy . . . you is gonna clean up that room. Okay?

ELLIE: [*Tough guy.*]   Oh Yeah? Who is gonna make me?

MAX: I am Louie, cause I am da tough cop in dis town. Now you is gonna get in dat cell and you is gonna clean it up, or else I is gonna throw you in solitary . . see?   [*They tussle for a moment, MAX pulls her cap over her eyes.*]

MAX: An I don't want to see you outta there till you is done. [*MAX shuts the door and exits.*]

ELLIE: Darn! Lately this place is really getting like a prison.

VOICE: Red Light! She keeps you locked up like some kind of prisoner.

ELLIE: Yeah! A prison with walls and bars and chains. A dungeon with cold stones and bread and water and rats. Solitary confinement . . The walls are closing in. You gotta let me out . . . You gotta let me out . . .

VOICE: Green Light!   [*Suddenly the toy lid flips open and a shovel full of dirt comes flying out. A shovel appears and on the other end of the shovel is LANA.*] *

ANA: Hi yah, Sweetie!

LLIE: Lana!

LANA: Who else? You think we wuz gonna let you take a bum rap? We
dug this tunnel t'bust you outta here.

ELLIE: We?

LANA: Frizbee and me! Right Frizbee? Frizbee? He was right behind me
in the tunnel. He must be here someplace. [*They look for FRIZBEE.
LANA looks in the toy chest and slams the lid.*]

LANA: Oh no!

ELLIE: What?

LANA: Don't look!

ELLIE: Why not?

LANA: Cave in! The tunnel's caved in.

ELLIE: Oh NO!

LANA: The whole thing. . . . Squash!

ELLIE: Poor Frizbee!

LANA: What are we gonna do?

ELLIE: There is only one thing we can do!

LANA: Yeah?

ELLIE: Blast!

LANA: Blast Boss?

ELLIE: It's the only way. You get the dynamite and I'll get the fuse. [*They
gather together junk to make a blasting box, fuse and plunger.*]

ELLIE: First you gotta make the box. Then you gotta put the dynamite in
and then stick your fingers in your ears, and count down
10,9,8,7,6,5,4,3,2. . . . 1 BARRROOOOOOOM. [*VOICE makes the
sound of the explosion. The lid flies open a puff of smoke comes out.
FRIZBEE'S arms and legs hang out of the box.*] ✱

FRIZBEE: [*Weakly*]   Hey you guys . . . . .

[*LANA and ELLIE rush to FRIZBEE and lift him out of the toy chest.*]

LANA: Are you alright?

FRIZBEE: Sure.

ELLIE: The tunnel collapsed on you.

FRIZBEE: I thought it got dark all of a sudden.

ELLIE: Okay. Youse guys we gotta blow this joint. [*FRIZBEE pulls a hand-kerchief out of costume and blows his nose, as he pulls another handker-chief comes out and a whole string of handkerchiefs follow to FRIZBEE'S amazement.*]

ELLIE: Great idea Frizbee. Here Lana you take one end and go first, I'll hold this, and Frizbee, you bring up the rear. Goodby cruel cell.*[*LANA and ELLIE dive into the box.*]

FRIZBEE: Goodbye cruel ceeeeeeee . . . . .

           [*FRIZBEE is pulled in after them. LUCILLE enters wearing a police hat and badge.*]

LUCILLE: Calling all cars. Calling all cars. This is the warden speaking! Ellie-the-mess-Murphy has just escaped from solitary confinement. She is messy and extremely dangerous. After her! After her! [*There is a chase. LANA and ELLIE crawl under the bed, and around the stage. LUCILLE crouches behind the bed.*]

LANA: We made it!

ELLIE: Free at last.

LANA: Wow that was close. [*LUCILLE appears.*]

LUCILLE: Have you cleaned up your room yet?

ELLIE AND LANA: EEEK! [*There is a short chase. LUCILLE lassos ELLIE and LANA with the scarfs and drags them over to one ·ide of the stage where she crouches down and VOICE makes the sound of a car. LUCILLE mimes driving the paddy wagon. FRIZBEE finally makes it out of the tunnel, sees what's going on, disappears for a second and reappears wearing the football helmet. VOICE makes the sound of a siren. FRIZBEE mimes riding a motorcycle. LUCILLE puts on the brakes. FRIZBEE gets off the motorcycle, pulls an imaginary pad out of his pocket licks an imaginary pencil.*]

FRIZBEE: Okay girlie, where's the fire?

LUCILLE: I'm sorry officer, I . . . . just wanted her to clean up her . . . .

FRIZBEE: Let me see your license. I'm gonna give you a ticket.

LUCILLE: But officer I . . . .

FRIZBEE: But first I'm gonna give you a . . . tickle.* [*FRIZBEE tickles LUCILLE, she laughs helplessly, LANA and ELLIE escape]

LUCILLE: You can't do that!

FRIZBEE: Oh yeah? I just did!

ELLIE: To the hideout! [LUCILLE chases them off. ELLIE, LANA and FRIZBEE race back to ELLIE'S room. They overturn the benches to make a barricade. ELLIE rifles through the toy chest throwing junk everywhere they put on guns and helmets.

ELLIE: Get the ammo and take cover.

VOICE: Come out with your hands up.

ELLIE: Let 'em have it.

[Imaginary battle takes place. They throw things all over the room. FRIZBEE uses a toilet paper roll like a grenade. ELLIE clutches a grease gun like a tommy gun. All make sounds. LUCILLE enters dressed in regular street clothes. She is not part of the fantasy.]

LUCILLE: [Approaching the door.] Ellinor, are you ready?

ELLIE: You'll never take us copper! [LUCILLE opens the door. All sound effects stop. LANA and FRIZBEE freeze. The room is totally destroyed. ELLIE pretends to be oiling the bed.

LUCILLE: [Dumbfounded] Ellinor.

ELLIE: I. . . I . . . I. uh, was just cleaning my room.

LUCILLE: Ellinor.

ELLIE: I didn't do it all. Lana threw the grenade.

LANA: I did not!

LUCILLE: I certainly hope you don't mean to tell me that Lana and Frizbee made all this mess.

ELLIE: What are you hoping I'll tell you?

LUCILLIE: Oh Ellinor.

ELLIE: They made most of it.

FRIZBEE: We did not!

LUCILLE: Are they supposed to be here now?

ELLIE: [Gesturing with grease gun.] They're right over . . . .

LUCILLE: Ellinor, that's a grease gun . . . . . don't . . . . . [ELLIE squeezes a glop of grease on the floor.]

VOICE: Glop!

ELLIE: Uh oh!

LUCILLE: The carpet! A brand new carpet! Grease is the worst possible stain. Oh my lord.

ELLIE: I thought it was empty.

LUCILLE: Now which is it hot water or cold? . . . . Oh my lord.

[LUCILLE rushes off to get a rag.]

LANA: Uhhhh so long Boss.

FRIZBEE: Be seeing you around.

ELLIE: Where are you going?

LANA: I just remembered something I gotta do.

FRIZBEE: Yeah and I gotta do it with her . . . . Whatever it is . . . . :THEY exit into the box. LUCILLE enters and rubs frantically at the spot.]

LUCILLE: It just gets worse and worse . . .It's ruined. A brand new carpet.

ELLIE: Well, I'm your brand new kid.

LUCILLE: Ellinor I knew something like this would happen. This is the last time you bring junk into your room. Oh it just gets bigger and bigger. [MAX enters, and rushes to help.]

MAX: What in the world . . . . . .

LUCILLE: Oh Max, Ellinor spilled grease on the carpet.

ELLIE: I didn't mean to.

LUCILLE: The more I rub the worse it gets.

ELLIE: It's not my fault.

MAX: Did you try cold water?

LUCILLE: No, it's hot water for grease.

ELLIE: Hey listen, I don't mind that spot.

MAX: No, I'm sure it's cold water.

ELLIE: Honest, I like that spot just the way it is.

LUCILLE: Max, it's hot water for grease and cold water for blood stains and ink.

MAX: I've got this stuff in my car.

LUCILLE: Oh it's no use!

ELLIE: [*Shouting*] Would you leave it alone! I like that spot. [*They both stop and stare at her.*] This is MY room.

LUCILLE: But it is a brand new carpet.

ELLIE: BIG DEAL.

MAX: Ellie, don't talk that way to your Mother.

ELLIE: She is not my real Mother. [*Stiff pause*]. [*To Lucille*] You'll never be my REAL MOTHER.

LUCILLE: (*Angry but even*) You know, Ellie, You're absolutely right. [*Pause*]

LUCILLE: [*Covering.*] Well if we are going to the market I better get my coat. [*LUCILLE exits. MAX is angry and very depressed.*]

MAX: That was nice. . . . that was really nice.

ELLIE: It's not my fault.

MAX: You hurt her feelings.

ELLIE: I have feelings too you know. Just because you're a kid doesn't mean you're junk!

MAX: Come off it Ellie.

ELLIE: That spot is almost out.

MAX: [*Really down*] Yeah!

ELLIE: Maybe we could put something over it.

MAX: Yeah.

ELLIE: With a sign that says "Don't look here."

MAX: [*With a slight laugh*] Sure.

ELLIE: [*Trying to get him out of his mood.*] Knock, knock.

MAX: Not now, Ellie.

ELLIE: Let's wrestle.

MAX: Uh uh!You're getting too big for me.

ELLIE: Do you think I'm too fat?

MAX: You? Naw you're fine.

ELLIE: Hey Pop, do you remember the time we went camping and you drove all afternoon to get out to the woods? It was dark when we pitched the tent and we heard all those funny sounds and you said it was MONSTERS. Then in the morning we found out we were in somebody's front lawn.

MAX: [*Responding a bit.*] I knew where we were all the time.

ELLIE: Or when we went to the Super Bowl and I got cold, and you said yell something in your megaphone.

MAX: Yeah, and you yelled "I'm cold and I want to go home." [*They both laugh.*]

ELLIE: [*Tentatively.*] Hey Pop, tell me about my real mother.

MAX: How come you want to hear about her all the time these days?
[*ELLIE sits at his feet and rests against his knees.*]

ELLIE: I just do. Hey do you remember the time it was my birthday and you brought Mom home from the hospital, and I didn't know she was coming that time? I remember I was already in bed and you guys wanted to surprise me. She just came into my room, kissed me goodnight and tucked me in, just like it was any other night.

MAX: [*Moved*] How could you remember that? You were just four years old.

ELLIE: I just remember.

MAX: Your mother was a wonderful person and I loved her very much.

ELLIE: As much as you . . . like Lucille?

MAX: Ellie.

ELLIE: Was she pretty?

MAX: She was beautiful.

ELLIE: Do I look like her?

MAX: Naw, you look more like me, you mug.

ELLIE: [*Suddenly angry*] Why does everything have to change?

MAX: Hey.

ELLIE: How come Lucille is always so neat and everything? I bet she never even burps.

MAX: She does.

ELLIE: HUH!

MAX: I heard her once.

ELLIE: Do you think I'd look cute with make-up on?

MAX: You? You're just a kid.

ELLIE: But Lucille wears make-up. Lot's of it.
MAX: Well she's grown up.

ELLIE: Hey do you know how old she is?

MAX: Sure. Thirty-five.

ELLIE: How come you married such an old one?

MAX: That's not old.

ELLIE: Huh!

MAX: Why I am older than that myself.
ELLIE: You are??

MAX: Ellie, you know how you get to go to camp in the summer. You get
to go away all by yourself.

ELLIE: Yeah but I'm not going any more.

MAX: You're not?

ELLIE: Nope, look what happened the last time I went. You and Lucille
get to be good friends, then as soon as I get back you get married. Who
knows if I go away again I might get back and find out you moved to
Alaska.

MAX: We wouldn't do that.

ELLIE: You might.

MAX: Ellie, kids can't always go where parents go. Sometimes parents go
away all by themselves.

ELLIE: How come ever since you got married I am such a kid. You never
used to say I was a kid. We did everything together. Now all I hear is,
"Kids can't do this," "Kids can't do that," "Kids have to go to bed at
eight-thirty." "Kids have to clean up their rooms." Why does everything
have to change?

MAX: Nothing's changed. I still love you the same. Now there's just two
of us who love you.

ELLIE: HUH!

POP: I just wish you'd try a little harder to . . . . .

ELLIE: To like Lucille? Why should I? She doesn't like me. She likes cute
little girls who play with dollies.

31

MAX: Well she got herself a messy little mug that likes junk. [*ELLIE pulls away.*]

MAX: I'm just kidding. She likes you fine the way you are.

ELLIE: Oh yeah, well I don't like her.

MAX: Why not?

[*LUCILLE enters and overhears the following.*]

ELLIE: Cause . . . Cause . . Cause she's a wicked stepmother . . . . [*ELLIE giggles in spite of herself. MAX is really angry.*[

MAX: That's not funny!

ELLIE: You shout at me all the time!

MAX: [*Shouting.*] I'm not shouting!

LUCILLE: [*Breaking it up.*] Is everybody ready to go?

MAX: Ellie get your coat.

ELLIE: I'm not going.

MAX: Get your coat. We are going for ice cream!

ELLIE: [*Pouting*] I don't want any.

MAX: Okay. Lucille let's go. Ellie you can just stay at home and clean up your room.

LUCILLE: Max . . . .

MAX: I said let's go!

ELLIE: See if I care.

[*They leave the room ELLIE pouts.*]

LUCILLE: Was it about the trip?

MAX: What?

LUCILLE: Were you two arguing about the trip?

MAX: Are you kidding, I didn't even get that far.

LUCILLE: Let's just forget it.

MAX: What?

LUCILLE: Forget the whole thing!

MAX: Oh no. I need this trip. We need it; we have got to have some time for US.

LUCILLE: If you want to go, then let's talk to her and we'll go. If not, let's just forget it!

MAX: Let me work this out in my own way.

LUCILLE: Why does everything have to be a game or a joke? Max, it really isn't fair to Ellie or me. Why can't we just talk?

MAX: This isn't easy for her.

LUCILLE: Well, it isn't easy for me either; and frankly, Max, I have just about had it.

MAX: Lucille . . .

LUCILLE: If we are ever going to be a family, we've got to be able to talk . . .

MAX: Not now! You're angry, she's angry. Let's go to the market, calm down, and we'll talk when we get home.

[They exit].

ELLIE: Hey, wait a minute. . . Wait, I changed my mind. I want to go.
     [They have gone. ELLIE turns back.]

VOICE: Red Light! It's all her fault! She didn't want you to go. SHE made it so you couldn't go.

     [ELLIE is drawn to the mirror.]

ELLIE and VOICE: Pick up your toys. Make your bed. Do what we say or you won't be fed.

ELLIE: I'll never be pretty. Ugly face, ugly hair and squinty little eyes. If I had my real mother I'd be pretty.

VOICE: You'll never be as pretty as Lucille. Green Light!

ELLIE: They dress me in rags. They make me work all day.

VOICE: Ugly Ellie.

ELLIE: Ugly Ellie, Ugly Ellie . . . *[ELLIE sits on the bed and pulls her cap over her face dejectedly.]

FRIZBEE: [Inside the toy box.] Cinderelli, Cinderelli, Cinderelli [Lid to the box opens and out pops FRIZBEE wearing Mickey Mouse ears and singing the Walt Disney song.]

FRIZBEE: Cinderelli, Cinderelli, Cinderelli, Cinderelli . . . .

ELLIE: What are you supposed to be?

FRIZBEE: I am just a little Mouse. Who lives inside this great big house. Oh Cinderelli kind and dear, I see what's been going on right here. Your wicked stepmother cruel and mean, Makes you wash and wax and clean. Now she's gone to the ice cream ball, And left you here with nothing at all.

ELLIE: Dear little Mouse you've seen everything?

FRIZBEE: Oh Yes! Everything and more.
Ever since your stepmother came to stay,
I have seen you slave all day.
She gives you crusts of bread to eat.
She pinches your elbows and stamps on your feet.
She gives you rags and paper towels to wear.
She calls you names and tangles your hair.

ELLIE: But what are we to do? I want to go to the ball but I have nothing to wear, my hair is dull, dull, dull, and my face is blah!

LANA: [From the toy box.] Perhaps there's something I can do.*[Toy box opens again, we see LANA'S feet waving in the air. ELLIE and FRIZBEE pull her out, she is outlandishly dressed in a gold lamee dress, blond wig, tiara, and silvery shoes.]

LANA: I am your fairy godmother and I have come to make you a star. We have much to do, after all stars are made not born.

ELLIE: Are you going to do a spell?

LANA: Oh no, spells are old fashioned. Today we have something much better . . . money! [LANA throws a fist-full of money in the air.]

34

LANA: First we need a dress.

ELLIE: Hey, I got an idea. Come with me. . . . .

[ELLIE leads them out of her room to LUCILLE'S ladder where she gets an elaborate party dress.]

LANA: Perfect!

FRIZBEE: But that's Lucille's.

LANA: Not anymore. We just bought it. [LANA spears a bill on the hanger and helps ELLIE on with the dress over her clothes.

LANA: And now the hair! Give her something that simply screams glamour.*[FRIZBEE becomes the hairdresser.]

FRIZBEE: Would Madame care for a flip?

[FRIZBEE does a flip.]
LANA: The hair you dolt! [LANA clobbers him. FRIZBEE makes an elaborate production of messing up ELLIE'S hair.]

LANA: Make-up! [FRIZBEE slaps make-up on ELLIE and shows her how to blot her lipstick by smacking her lips. He gets carried away with the smacking and gives LANA a big kiss.]

LANA: Oh gross! [LANA clobbers him.]

LANA: And now the coach. [FRIZBEE puts on the football helmet and jumps around being a coach.]

LANA: THE CARRIAGE ! ! [FRIZBEE gets a broomstick horse.]

LANA: And last but not least. . . your public! [LANA throws a fist full of money in the air and there is tumultuous cheering.]

[ELLIE, FRIZBEE and LANA exit in procession. A fanfare is heard. FRIZBEE enters with a roll of paper towels which he rolls out like a red carpet. He stands at attention at the end of the carpet. LANA swirls on and down the carpet, she curtsies to FRIZBEE.]

VOICE: Ladies and gentlemen, the Prince. [MAX enters dressed in a frock coat over his regular clothes. He bows and stands at the end of the "carpet."]

VOICE: And now ladies and gentlemen, the moment we have all been waiting for, the star of stage, screen and television. . . the Princess Cinderelli! [*Music plays the Sleeping Beauty Waltz, ELLIE enters, a spot light catches her, she sweeps down the carpet to MAX who bows. They dance.*]

LANA: [*As they waltz by her.*] Remember darling, your contract is up at midnight. [*VOICE begins to bang on a pot with a spoon, twelve times in all. On the stroke of twelve LUCILLE appears, sweeps down the "carpet." MAX turns and bows to her and dances off with her leaving ELLIE.*]

ELLIE: Hey wait a minute, what do you think you're doing? [*LANA and FRIZBEE exit.*]

ELLIE: Hey, I'm supposed to be the Princess around here. Hey, I'm Cinderelli! Come back. Alright see if I care. I don't need any stupid old prince. I can have a good time all by myself. [*ELLIE sings and dances all by herself. Music out, ELLIE, obviously upset, dances faster and faster. MAX and LUCILLE enter with groceries. They stop at her door and watch. MAX bursts out laughing. LUCILLE elbows him. ELLIE stops, mortified at being caught.*]

ELLIE: Well what are you staring at?

MAX: What is this, Halloween?

ELLIE: What's so funny?

LUCILLE: I think you look very pretty.

ELLIE: [*Defensive.*] Well I wasn't trying to look pretty! I was trying to look dumb and funny, like this. . and this. . and this . . . [*ELLIE makes faces.*]

Since I can't be pretty I might as well be funny and dumb. [*ELLIE capers around wildly until she stubs her toe.*]

ELLIE: Owwwwwwww!

LUCILLE: What's the matter?

ELLIE: I stubbed my dumb toe. [*ELLIE sits and buries her head in her hands. MAX starts to go to her. LUCILLE stops him by shoving her sack of groceries into his arms.*

LUCILLE: Max, will you put these in the kitchen for me? [*MAX gives her a look, she waves him away and he exits. LUCILLE goes to ELLIE and helps her out of the dress.*]

36

LUCILLE: You okay? [*ELLIE pulls away and sits on the bed. She shrugs.*]

LUCILLE: Ellinor, if I asked you to help me with something would you do it?

ELLIE: I didn't clean up my room.

LUCILLE: So I see, but that's not what I am talking about. I want you to help me with something else.

ELLIE: Huh! I don't see what I could help you do.

LUCILLE: [*Tentatively*] Well, I've never had any children. . .and lots of times I'm not too sure what mothers are supposed to do. So I wanted you to help me.

ELLIE: How should I know? I never really had a mother, not one I remember real well.

LUCILLE: Well, maybe we could help each other. [*ELLIE shrugs.*]

LUCILLE: You see, my mother was very strict. She made me pick up my room and practice my voice every day and I loved her.

ELLIE: She was your real mother.

LUCILLE: Yes.

ELLIE: That makes a difference. You have to love your real mother and your real kids.

LUCILLE: But you can choose to love your stepchildren.

ELLIE: But nobody can make you.

LUCILLE: [*Pause.*] That's right.

ELLIE: Well I can tell you a couple of things mothers shouldn't do. They shouldn't try to make their kids different from the way they are. Like if the kid is messy, they shouldn't try to make them be neat. And mothers shouldn't make their kids go to bed at eight-thirty, especially when there's good movies on T.V.

LUCILLE: But what if the mother wants the child to be healthy and she thinks the child should get some sleep?

ELLIE: Who's supposed to be doing the helping around here, you or me?

LUCILLE: Sorry.

ELLIE: Mothers should love their kids no matter what. Even if the kid is funny and dumb and looks like a gorilla; Mothers should make them think they are beautiful.

LUCILLE: But what if the. .kid won't let the mother. . . .

ELLIE: Mothers gotta go first! That's the rules.

LUCILLE: Ellie. . .I. . . .

ELLIE: [*Turning away.*] What's for supper?

LUCILLE: Huh?

ELLIE: I'm getting hungry. What's for supper?

LUCILLE: I thought I'd make a beef stroganoff.

ELLIE: What's that?

LUCILLE: It's little slices of beef with sour cream and. . . . .

ELLIE: SOUR CREAM! UHHHHHH! Mothers should never make their kids eat SOUR CREAM! [*ELLIE clutches her throat.*]

LUCILLE: [*Laughing*] You should try it.

ELLIE: I know, Why don't I make dinner tonight? I used to do that all the time. Pop and I had this really neat game we'd play. First we'd cook up a whole bunch of T.V. dinners and then we'd put on blindfolds and try to guess what we were eating.

MAX: [*Entering*] Did I hear somebody mention food?

LUCILLE: I just had a great idea! Why don't we eat out tonight?

ELLIE: Knock knock. . .

MAX: Who's there?
ELLIE: Uda.

MAX: Uda who?

ELLIE: [*Singing*] "You deserve a break today". . . . .

MAX: [*Joining in*] . . ."So go on and get away to MacDonalds."** [*MAX encourages LUCILLE to join in*]

LUCILLE: But I don't know the words.

ELLIE: It's simple. But you can't sing it in that toot toot de doot voice. You gotta do it like this. . . [*ELLIE belts it out.*]

ELLIE: "You deserve a break today. So go on and get away to MacDonalds."

LUCILLE: [*Belting*] Like this? "You deserve a break today. So go on and get away to MacDonalds." [*They all join in on the last line.*]

ELLIE: Not bad, for a beginner.

MAX: Let's go.

LUCILLE: Wait a minute, I have to put the meat in the freezer. [*LUCILLE exits.*]

MAX: Hey Ellie, after supper how about a little. . . [*MAX mimes bowling*]

ELLIE: Great! Just you and me, like the old days?

MAX: Ellie?

ELLIE: Oh I bet Lucille doesn't even know how to bowl. I bet she thinks it is a dirty smelly sport.

MAX: Oh, come on.

ELLIE: Oh, I guess she can come.

MAX: If she doesn't know you'll have to teach her.

ELLIE: Yeah, I could. Cause if there is one thing I do know it is bowling. [*LUCILLE enters.*]

MAX: Lucille, would you like to go bowling after supper?

**This jingle should be constantly updated to any popular theme song of a fast food chain.*

LUCILLE: Oh Max, I was hoping we could all come back here and.
     TALK.

MAX: [Ignoring the hint] Oh yeah, yeah. We can do that afterward.

LUCILLE: Maybe just you two should go. I've never bowled before and I
     wouldn't want to slow you down.

MAX: Baloney! There's nothing to it. We'll show you. Right Midget?
     [ELLIE shrugs and MAX elbows her.]

ELLIE: Sure, sure, it just takes practice, to get good that is. I'll show you.

MAX: Let's go. [They start out.]

ELLIE: Wait a sec, let me get my shoes.

MAX: We'll meet you in the car.

     [MAX and LUCILLE exit. ELLIE gets her bowling shoes from under the
     bed and starts out.]

VOICE: Red Light![ELLIE freezes.]

VOICE: You aren't going to fall for all that stuff are you?

ELLIE: Huh?

VOICE: All that "Help me be a mother" stuff?

ELLIE: Well. . .

VOICE: Stepmothers always say that. . . to soften you up. They don't
     really mean that. And now she's going bowling with you. And after you
     teach her you know what will happen? She and Fop will go and leave you
     home . . . alone. Green Light!

MAX: *[Off stage] Come on Ellie![ELLIE hesitates and exits. By minor
     adjustments in the set it switches to the bowling alley. The sound of balls
     rolling and pins falling can be heard all through the next scene. As soon as
     the scene is shifted ELLIE, MAX, and LUCILLE enter. ELLIE munches a
     bag of french fries, they cross to benches set up to indicate their alley.
     MAX sets up a score sheet, changes his shoes. All bowling should be
     mimed.

40

MAX: Why don't we take a couple of practice shots? Will you show Lucille how to hold the ball while I get us squared away?

ELLIE: [*Licking her fingers*] Okay, first you get a ball. . . [*ELLIE points, LUCILLE looks a bit apprehensive but she gets a ball.*]

MAX: [*Under his breath*] Ellie, I want you to be nice.

ELLIE: [*Slaps on a huge smile*] I am being nice. . .SEE? Now you hold the ball like this with three fingers. . . That's good. . . very very good! And you look right at that center pin and bring your hand straight back. . like this and you just swing through. . . . See?

LUCILLE: [*Gamely*] Sure I think so. . .

ELLIE: Well go ahead . . . Try one. [*LUCILLE follows all ELLIE's instructions but the unexpected weight of the ball throws her off balance. Finally she manages to bowl one ball but very badly. There is the sound of a gutterball.*]

ELLIE: [*Much too nice.*] Good! VERY GOOD Lucille. [*ELLIE smirks.*]

MAX: Lucille, that's called a gutterball, and it's not good. Ellie I'll show her. Why don't you take your turn?

ELLIE: Can I have a Coke?

LUCILLE: You just finished dinner.

ELLIE: Pop?

MAX: Yeah sure, here's fifteen cents.

[*ELLIE walks away a few steps. MAX moves over to LUCILLE and shows her how to hold the ball, very cozily. ELLIE returns.*]

ELLIE: AHEM! I believe it is MY turn. [*ELLIE takes a ball and goes through a very elaborate warm-up.*]

MAX: [*Quitely*] Now you see you just bring the ball straight back and . . .

LUCILLE: Where is the aiming? [*ELLIE bowls just as LUCILLE is talking, she slips a little and is thrown off. There is the sound of a few pins falling.*]

ELLIE: No fair! No fair! You're not supposed to talk! You threw me off!

MAX: [*Writing down the score.*] Uhhh, three! A little to the left.

ELLIE: That's not fair.

MAX: Oh go on, you've still got another ball.

ELLIE: This time NO talking. [*ELLIE bowls. All pins fall.*]

MAX: Fantastic.

LUCILLE: Nice aiming, Ellinor. That was a good shot wasn't it dear?

ELLIE: [*Cocky*] You bet. That's what you call a spare. It is just about the
           best you can do. Of course it takes hours and hours of practice.

MAX: Nice one Midget! Okay Lucille, it's all yours. Just relax and
           concentrate. [*LUCILLE starts into the backswing.*]

ELLIE: Hold IT!

[*LUCILLE stops clumsily.*]

ELLIE: This is the foul line. If you step over it nothing counts. . . . I was
           just trying to help! [*LUCILLE bowls, very awkwardly. Sound of ball rolling
           very slowly.*]

ELLIE: [*Watching the ball.*] Don't expect too much, not right at first.
           After all there is only one thing better than a spare and that's a. . . [*Sound
           of pins falling domino effect. ELLIE'S face contorts in utter amazement.*]

ELLIE: A STRIKE?????
MAX: Fantastic!

LUCILLE: Is that good?

MAX: You bet it is!

ELLIE: I think I'm going to be sick!

LUCILLE: What does that little X mean up there?

ELLIE: [*Nasty*] It means a strike!

MAX: Not bad, old lady, not bad at all.

[*ELLIE starts coughing real fakey.*]

LUCILLE: Beginner's luck.

MAX: Let's see. My turn now. [*ELLIE coughs.*]

MAX: What's the matter with you?

ELLIE: I don't feel so good.

MAX: Well lie down for a minute.

ELLIE: I don't exactly feel like bowling. [*MAX shoots her a look which silences her. MAX picks up the ball and lines up the shot, very machismo. Just as he bowls ELLIE coughs and throws him off. He gets a gutterball.*]

MAX: Ellie!

ELLIE: [*Innocently*] Sorry.

LUCILLE: What's the matter Ellinor?

MAX: Nothing's the matter. She's just got a bad case of fakeitus that's all!

ELLIE: By the way, Lucille, that's called a gutterball, it's not good.

MAX: Now, no more talking, noisemaking, sneezing, coughing or anything. [*MAX lines up the shot and ELLIE yawns.*]

MAX: One more noise out of you and it's out to the car. [*MAX takes his time lining up the shot, ELLIE picks up her Coke can which she opens just as he bowls. The can explodes in a spray of Coke. MAX tosses his ball over several lanes. He is furious.*]

ELLIE: Ooops!

MAX: ELLIE!

LUCILLE: Good Lord it is all over everything!

ELLIE: I couldn't help it.

MAX: You did that on purpose 'cause you're a rotten sport.

ELLIE: I did not.

MAX: Out to the car!

ELLIE: POP!

MAX: I said out to the car!

LUCILLE: Dear!

MAX: I am not going to have her wreck our game just because she's a lousy sport.

LUCILLE: Let's go home.

MAX: WHAT?

LUCILLE: I don't really care about bowling.

MAX: Well I do. Ellie out to the car. I said it and I meant it.

LUCILLE: You can't send her out there to wait in a dark parking lot.

MAX: Oh yes I can. We are going to finish this game, and Ellie is going to wait for us out in the car. If there is one thing I can't stand it is a rotten sport.

LUCILLE: I will not permit you to send that child out there alone.

MAX: It's just out to the car, do you want me to hire a babysitter?

ELLIE: [*Embarrassed.*] Pop!

LUCILLE: Max, keep your voice down. We'll settle this when we get home.

MAX: Are you telling me how to discipline my kid?

LUCILLE: You? You're a fine one to talk about discipline. Why you're a bigger kid than she is. Why we should all be sitting at home right now having a family discussion. But Oh no! We have to get ice cream. We all have to go bowling first. . . all because you can't even talk to your own child. . . .

MAX: [*Impulsive*] Oh you don't think I can tell her . . . [*MAX crosses to ELLIE, LUCILLE tries to stop him.*]

LUCILLE: Max, not here and not now. . . Let's go home.

MAX: [*To Ellie.*] Ellie, we are going to Hawaii!

[To Lucille] There! Now are you satisfied? *[LUCILLE is horrified. MAX realizes instantly that he has really blown it.]*

LUCILLE: Oh MAX!

ELLIE: What are you guys talking about?

MAX: *[Fighting his way out.]* Uhhh, Ellie, we are going away. . . We're going to Hawaii.

ELLIE: HAWAII?

MAX: Yeah, for about three weeks.

ELLIE: Neato! Do I get to get out of school?

MAX: No Ellie, just Lucille and I are going. I was gonna tell you all about it when we got home tonight, well now you know.

ELLIE: What. . .What about me?

MAX: Well you kind of like Mrs. Dougan and I thought maybe she'd come and. . .

ELLIE: You are going away and leaving me.
LUCILLE: Ellie. . .

ELLIE: *[Getting mad.]* So that's what all that sneaking around was about! So that's what all those papers and secret stuff was about. You guys are going away and leaving me.
LUCILLE: Ellinor, that's not. . . .

ELLIE: *[Turns on her.]* And YOU! All that "Help me be a mother," stuff! That was just to soften me up. Well I'll tell you one thing mothers shouldn't do, mothers shouldn't lie to their kids about all that love stuff and then dump them.
MAX: Ellie, stop shouting.

ELLIE: I should have known. I should have known you didn't really like me. You just wanted to have POP all to yourself. Well go ahead! See if I care!

MAX: Ellie, we are going home. Take off your shoes and wait for me in the car.

ELLIE: You can't just throw me out like the trash you know.

MAX: ELLIE OUT TO THE CAR! [*ELLIE starts to run out. MAX stops her.*]

MAX: Ellie, your shoes! [*ELLIE, furious, takes off her shoes and throws them at him and runs out. LUCILLE looks at MAX for a minute.*]

LUCILLE: Well you certainly handled that one well.

MAX: Lay off! Oh I'm sorry, I didn't mean for this to happen.

LUCILLE: I should hope not. Max, discipline isn't something you turn off and on like hot water.

MAX: I know.

LUCILLE: [*Taking off her shoes and exiting.*] We were just beginning. After two months we were just beginning. [*LUCILLE exits. MAX sits for a minute. He picks up the score sheet and crumples it. He starts out when LUCILLE enters at a run.*]

LUCILLE: Max, she isn't there! She's gone!

MAX: What?

LUCILLE: She's run away. She left this note on the windshield.

[*LUCILLE hands MAX a note.*]

MAX: [*Reading*] "You win Lucille."

LUCILLE: [*Panicing*] Where could she have gone?

MAX: Anywhere! Let's go, she can't have gotten too far. [*LUCILLE sees ELLIE'S shoes.*]

LUCILLE: Oh Max, she hasn't even got her shoes on.

MAX: Come on. [*MAX and LUCILLE exit. Weird sounds begin, the recorded voices of LANA, FRIZBEE and VOICE are heard chanting "Run away." The following scene is a mixture of fantasy and reality. A sound collage of voices and scarey music form the background.*]

VOICE, LANA and FRIZBEE: Run away. . .Run away. . .Run away. . .Run away. . . . *

[ELLIE enters at a run. LANA and FRIZBEE enter also but they appear as strange menacing figures, such as a stop sign that is knocked over, a staggering drunk, a car that nearly runs ELLIE down.]

VOICE, LANA and FRIZBEE: Run away. Run away. Run away. Run away.
There's a fact you've go to face. . .
Run away. Run away.
That she's taken your place. . .
Run away. Run away.

VOICE, LANA and FRIZBEE: [Recorded] And there's nothing you can do . . . Run away, Run away. Cause he loves her more than you . . . Run away, Run away.

ELLIE: I'll show you. Boy will you be sorry! I'm never going home. [A cat yeowls and LUCILLE appears dressed in a long black cloak.]

LUCILLE: [Recorded.] Mirror, mirror, on the wall, who's the fairest of them all?

ELLIE: I am, you wicked old stepmother! [ELLIE runs into FRIZBEE who holds a newspaper in front of his face.]

FRIZBEE: Go home little girl.

ELLIE: I'm never going home. I'll find some new parents.

[ELLIE runs over to LANA who is wearing a farmer's hat and mimes churning butter.]

ELLIE: Will you adopt a poor orphan child?

LANA: [Malevolently] My lands, who is this child?

ELLIE: I am just a poor orphan with no father or mother.

FRIZBEE: [Also wearing a farmer's hat.] I see the mark of the princess Cinderelli upon her cheek. We will adopt you.

ELLIE: I am not the princess, I'm just Ellie, Ellie Murphy.

FRIZBEE: Well, if you are not the princess then get lost. [ELLIE staggers away from them.]

ELLIE: I'm not scared. I'm not scared. I'm not scared. Oh, my feet are so cold. [*MAX enters slowly with his back to the audience. He wears a raincoat with a hood. LUCILLE enters with her back to the audience, she too wears a long coat.*]

ELLIE: Pop! Is that you Pop? Hey!

MAX: [*Still with his back to her.*] I beg your pardon?

ELLIE: Pop! It's me, Ellie.

MAX: I'm sorry but I don't believe I know you.

ELLIE: Pop, It's me, your daughter! Ellie!

MAX: Who?

ELLIE: Hey Lucille! It's me, Ellie.

LUCILLE: [*Still with her back to her.*] I beg your pardon?

ELLIE: Look at me! It's Ellie!

LUCILLE: I don't believe I know you. [*Slowly they turn to look at her. They wear half-masks which are transparent.*]

LUCILLE: Do you know this child?

MAX: No, I'm sorry little girl.

LUCILLE: Come dear, we have a plane to catch.

MAX: Oh yes, we mustn't be late.

LUCILLE: [*As they exit*] What a strange little girl.

ELLIE: Don't you know me? I'm your child! [*Strange music and recorded voices begin again. LANA and FRIZBEE step in and out of the shadows moving in slow motion.*]

VOICE, LANA and FRIZBEE: [*Recorded*] You're alone. . . You're alone.

LANA: [*Like a cat yeowl*] Hi ya Sweetie. . . .

VOICE, LANA and FRIZBEE: [*Recorded*] Can't go home. . . Can't go home. . .

ELLIE: Doesn't anybody know me?

LANA: Hi ya Boss. . .

ELLIE: I'm not the Boss. I'm. . .

VOICE, LANA and FRIZBEE: [Recorded] You're alone. . . You're alone.

FRIZBEE: Singer of the year. . .

ELLIE: I don't want to be. . .

VOICE, LANA and FRIZBEE: Got no home . . . Got no home . . .

ELLIE: I don't want to be an orphan.

VOICE, LAND and FRIZBEE: You're alone. . . You're alone. . .
All alone . . . All alone. .

ELLIE: I just want to go home. [ELLIE runs around the stage, as she does
the scene is shifted back to her house. ELLIE enters the living room area
and looks around.]

ELLIE: I'm home! Hey Pop? Lucille? I'm home. I don't want to be an
orphan. Pop? LUCILLE ? [ELLIE sighs and goes into her room. She throws
herself down on her bed and falls into a deep sleep.] *

[Soft music begins, a lullabye played on a music box. ELLIE dreams and in
her dream MAX and LUCILLE enter wearing dressing gowns. LANA and
FRIZBEE enter. They carry windchimes which tinkle softly. During this
scene the words must tumble and flow like a waterfall, nothing
frightening. It is a soft and gentle dream.]

LUCILLE: Shhhhh. Don't wake the baby. . . .

FRIZBEE: What a beautiful baby. . .

LANA: What a good baby. . .

MAX: Daddy's beautiful baby girl.

ELLIE: [Recorded] I never had a Mother, not one I remember real well.

LANA: Sleep. . .

FRIZBEE: . . . Dream.

ELLIE: [*Recorded*] Mother? Mother? Where are you? It's dark. I'm scared.
[*LUCILLE billows a soft coverlet and covers ELLIE.*]

LUCILLE: Shall I tell you a story? Shall I sing you a song?

ELLIE: [*Recorded*] I can't see myself. I'm messy. I'm mean.

LANA: Sleep. . .

FRIZBEE: . . .Dream.

MAX: Daddy's pretty Ellie.

ELLIE: [*Recorded*] Mother tell me a story. Mother sing me a song.

[*LUCILLE begins to hum softly.*]
LANA: Sleep. . .

FRIZBEE: . . .Dream.

ELLIE: Can you be my mother?

LUCILLE: Sleep. . .

ELLIE: Please be my mother.

MAX: . . .Dream.

ELLIE: I want to have a mother!

LANA: Shhh. Don't wake the child.

FRIZBEE: What a beautiful child.

MAX: Daddy's beautiful girl.

LUCILLE: Pretty Ellie. . .

MAX and LUCILLE: [*Recorded*] Pretty Ellie. . .Pretty Ellie. . .Pretty Ellie. .
Pretty Ellie. [*All exit slowly as the recorded music and sound continue for
a moment. ELLIE tosses and turns on the bed. The dream fades and the
house returns to normal. MAX enters the house dressed as he was at the
bowling alley. He is upset and in a hurry.*]

MAX: I know I have a recent photograph around here somewhere. Lucille
you call the police; say you want to report a missing person. [*LUCILLE
enters.*]

LUCILLE: I just don't understand how she could have gotten so far so quickly. Oh Max, what are we going to do?

MAX: I know we had some pictures taken at Woolworths right before she left for camp. Where did I put them?

LUCILLE: She's been gone two hours. Anything could have happened.

MAX: Take it easy. We'll find her. She's probably just hiding in a restaurant or something. You call the police. I'll go back to the bowling alley.

LUCILLE: I can't help feeling this is all my fault.

MAX: Maybe they are in her room. Call the police. [*MAX enters ELLIE'S room. He stops dead when he sees her asleep. He is unable to speak for a second and sighs in relief.*]

MAX: [*Very calmly*] Lucille. [*LUCILLE crosses to him. He points to the sleeping figure. LUCILLE crouches by the bed.*]

LUCILLE: Thank God.

MAX: Let's let her sleep. She must be exhausted. [*They leave the room and close the door behind them.*]

LUCILLE: She must have walked all this way.

MAX: She must have run.

LUCILLE: [*Still slightly hysterical*] Thank God she's alright. Anything could have happened to her. I don't know what I would have done if. . .

[*ELLIE wakes up, sits and listens.*]

MAX: Hey, calm down. Everything is alright now.

LUCILLE: She could have been killed. What if she'd gotten hit by a car?

MAX: [*Firmly*] Lucille, it is all over now. Take it easy. She's home. I'll get something to relax you, just a minute. [*MAX exits. ELLIE gets out of bed and starts toward the door.*]

VOICE: Red Light!

[*ELLIE freezes.*]

VOICE: Where are you going?

ELLIE: Out there.

VOICE: Why?

ELLIE: To tell them I'm. . .

VOICE: You could have been killed and its all HER fault. She almost got rid of you once and for all.

ELLIE: But she really sounded worried.

VOICE: You aren't going to fall for that stuff again are you? She just said that so Pop wouldn't be mad at her. She's trying to get rid of you.

ELLIE: Aww that's dumb.

VOICE: You could have been killed and she'd live happily ever after with Pop. That's how wicked stepmothers are you know.

ELLIE: But. . .

VOICE: You could have been killed and she'd live happily after after with Pop. That's how wicked stepmothers are you know.

ELLIE: But . . .

VOICE: You could have been killed. Green Light!

[MAX enters with a drink for LUCILLE.]

MAX: Here, this will calm you down. Everything is going to be alright.

LUCILLE: Thanks. I've been thinking, Max, may I should go away.

MAX: What?

LUCILLE: Maybe I should just let you and Ellie work things out alone. I kept hoping it was just a matter of time . . . that gradually she would come to accept me.

MAX: You're just upset.

LUCILLE: I care for both of you too much to see you destroy what you had together. Maybe I should just leave for a while.

MAX: That's crazy. We are a family now and we are going to work through this thing, all of us, together. Your leaving isn't going to help.

LUCILLE: I don't know.

MAX: Well, I do.

LUCILLE: She must have loved her real Mother very much to hate me so.

MAX: She doesn't hate you. She's just mixed up right now. It's late and we are tired. Let's talk about this in the morning.

LUCILLE: No, I really think it would be better for me to leave you two alone for a while to work things out any way you can.

MAX: Let's go to bed.

[MAX exits. LUCILLE picks up the note ELLIE left on the windshield and reads.]

LUCILLE: "You win, Lucille." *[She looks toward Ellie's room.]* No, Ellie, YOU win. *[She exits]*.

[ELLIE is disturbed by this and she starts out the door after them.]

ELLIE: Hey you guys. . .

VOICE: Red Light! *[ELLIE freezes.]*

VOICE: Congratulations! You won!

ELLIE: But she's leaving.

VOICE: That's what you wanted isn't it? Now you and Pop can go back to having things the way they used to be.

ELLIE: Yeah but. . .

VOICE: After all, she wanted to get rid of you. She wanted you to get killed, and then you could have had a funeral.

ELLIE: A funeral? *

VOICE: Yeah a funeral. At funerals everybody is real sorry for all the mean things they ever did to you. Everybody just sits around and says nice things about you and they cry and cry and cry. [*FRIZBEE starts to sniffle.*]

ELLIE: What about Pop?

VOICE: He cries the loudest of all. [*FRIZBEE bursts into sobs.*]

ELLIE: What am I supposed to do?

VOICE: Well, first you gotta have a coffin. [*LANA and FRIZBEE move the toy box forward for the coffin.*]

VOICE: You just lie there.

ELLIE: Suppose I want to see what's going on.

VOICE: No, you gotta just lie there.

ELLIE: That sound stupid. Hey, I got an idea. Why don't you lie there and be me in the coffin.

VOICE: No, I stay right here.

ELLIE: Get in that coffin!

VOICE: Okay. . .Okay. . . Green Light [*VOICE lies on the box and ELLIE takes charge of the microphone.*]

ELLIE: Okay ladies and gentlemen. Let's get this show on the road. Ellie Murphy's funeral. . .Take One! [*LANA and FRIZBEE clap their hands like a claque board.*]

ELLIE: Now the parade starts over there. I want a black horse with a plume. [*FRIZBEE puts a plume on his head and neighs.*]

ELLIE: Fantastic! I want music, drums sad and slow! That's right. [*LANA wearing a long black veil falls into a procession behind FRIZBEE and they both wail.*]

ELLIE: Now start with the nice things.

LANA: She was so young and so beautiful. . .

ELLIE: Cut! Lana, honey, more tears. . .that's right cry, cry, cry. Now throw yourself over the coffin. Preacher that's your cue. [*FRIZBEE becomes the preacher.*]

FRIZBEE: Poor Ellie Murphy! Why didn't I tell her how cute she was and what nice straight teeth she had.

ELLIE: Come on preacher, nicer things!

FRIZBEE: Poor Ellie Murphy. Why didn't I tell her how pretty she was, what a good voice she had. She was the best bowler I ever saw!

ELLIE: Pop! You're on! [*MAX enters wearing pajamas and a high silk hat, and black arm bands.*

MAX: I'm sorry Ellie.

ELLIE: More feeling Pop!

MAX: I'M SORRY ELLIE!!!! How could I have been so blind? I never needed anyone but you. Now my life is empty, bleak, bland. . .

ELLIE: From the bottom of your heart, Pop!

MAX: What a fool I have been and now it is too late!!!

ELLIE: And now for the final touch! Lucille enters up right, rubbing her hand and laughing. [*ELLIE indicates up right. Nothing happens.*]

ELLIE: I said, the grand finale. . . LUCILLE enters up right, rubbing her hands and laughing. [*ELLIE indicates up right again and LUCILLE enters up left. She wears a coat and carries a suitcase.*]

LUCILLE: I have been thinking, Max, maybe I should go away.

ELLIE: No, CUT! Lucille enters up right, rubbing her hands and laughing.

LUCILLE: Maybe I should let you and Ellie work things out alone.

ELLIE: I said, up right!

LUCILLE: I kept hoping that it was just a matter of time.

ELLIE: Cut! Cut! You are not supposed to be saying that!

LUCILLE: I kept hoping that gradually she would come to accept me.

ELLIE: You are supposed to be glad that I'm dead.

LUCILLE: I care for you both too much to see you destroy what you had together. Maybe I should just leave.

ELLIE: You are not supposed to be saying that!

LUCILLE: She must have loved her real mother very much to hate me so. So I'm leaving.

ELLIE: Hey wait, Lucille.

LUCILLE: No Ellie, YOU win.

ELLIE: Wait I didn't mean for it to go this far.

VOICE: Red Light! [*ELLIE freezes.*]

VOICE: Don't call her back. You've won! Now things will be the way they always have been.

ELLIE: Why don't you shut up! You are supposed to be dead! I want a mother and she's a perfectly good one.

VOICE: But she's a wicked step. . . .

ELLIE: **RED LIGHT!** [*VOICE freezes.*]

ELLIE: Lana, Frizbee, take that thing away. Green Light! [*LANA and FRIZBEE move like puppets. They move VOICE back to the stool and move the toy box back into its place.*]

ELLIE: Now get in.* [*ELLIE helps them both into the toy box. She closes the lid and sits on the box for a second.*]

ELLIE: Lucille! Lucille! Come back! [*ELLIE moves back into bed as LUCILLE and MAX enter her room. They both wear the dressing gowns seen in the dream scene.*]

MAX: [*Entering first*] Ellie? What's the matter?

ELLIE: Where is Lucille?

LUCILLE: [*Entering*] Right here. What's the matter?

ELLIE: [*Relieved*] Oh. . . uhhh, nothing. I must have had a bad dream.

MAX: Do you want to tell me about it?

ELLIE: I don't thing you'd like it.

MAX: Is it alright now?

ELLIE: Yeah. I guess so.

MAX: Well, goodnight Midget.

[*MAX kisses her on the forehead.*]

ELLIE: Goodnight Pop. [*MAX and LUCILLE turn to leave.*]

ELLIE: Uhhh Lucille? [*MAX stays in the doorway and LUCILLE crosses to her.*]

LUCILLE: Yes?

ELLIE: I'm. . . sorry I ran away.

LUCILLE: So am I.

ELLIE: Well, I'm back now.

LUCILLE: I'm glad.

ELLIE: So am I. [*Pause.*]

ELLIE: Uhhh Lucille, I'm cold.

LUCILLE: Well no wonder, you kicked your covers off. [*LUCILLE billows the covers over her and tucks her in. EILLIE smiles.*]

ELLIE: Uhh Lucille, knock, knock. . .

LUCILLE: Who's there?

ELLIE: Sticker.

LUCILLE: Sticker who?

ELLIE: Sticker-ound for a while, okay?

LUCILLE: Okay. Goodnight Ellie. Sleep well.* [*LUCILLE moves away a few steps and crouches.*]

LUCILLE: Goodnight Lana. Goodnight Frizbee.

ELLIE: Uhhh Lucille, they're not here.

LUCILLE: Oh. [*LUCILLE crosses to MAX and turns back.*]

LUCILLE: Goodnight Ellie.

ELLIE: [*Pulling the covers up and turning over.*] See ya in the morning.

BLACK OUT

NOTES

NOTES

NOTES

NOTES

NOTES

NOTES